FIRE ENGINES

Illustrated by Tibor Gergely

A GOLDEN BOOK • NEW YORK
Western Publishing Company, Inc., Racine, Wisconsin 53404

Ding, ding, ding! goes the alarm.

The fire fighters slide down the pole.

Clang, clang, clang! goes the fire engine bell.

The chief is on the way.

Here they come!

Watch out! Make way for the hose car.

Hurry, hurry! Jump on the hook-and-ladder truck!

The people come running out to see

the great big hook-and-ladder truck.

Here they are at the fire.

The chief tells the fire fighters what to do.

Quick! Connect the hoses!

S-s-s-s! goes the water.

Crank, crank. Up go the ladders.

Up go the fire fighters with their hoses.

Chop, chop, chop! go the axes.

Crash! go the windows.

Down the ladders come the fire fighters.

They jump into the net to save things from the fire!

Sput, sput, sput! Out goes the fire.

Tired fire fighters and people go home.

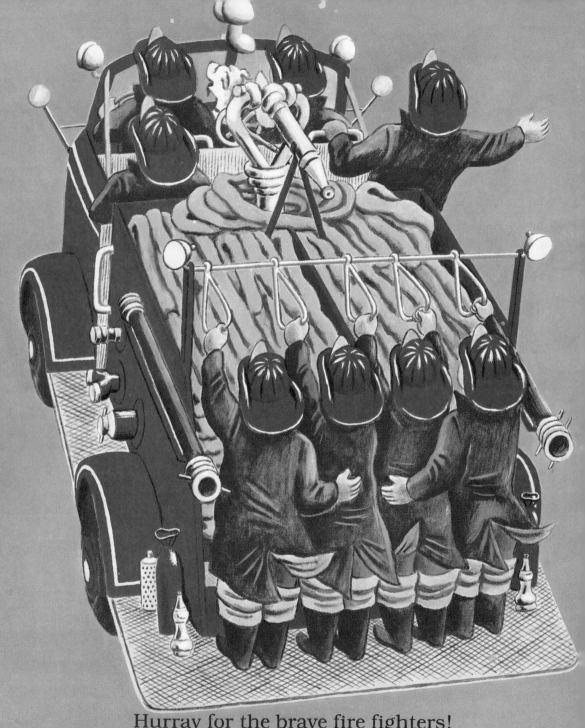

Hurray for the brave fire fighters!